ne USA
rmation can be obtained
Gtesting.com
231040124
V00044B/797

UNLIKE HER *GONE WITH THE WIND* HEROINE, SCARLETT O'HARA, MARGARET MITCHELL WAS NOT SELFISH OR BROODING.

BUT LIKE SCARLETT, MARGARET WAS A COMPLEX WOMAN LIVING IN A DIFFICULT TIME.

PERHAPS THIS RESILIENCE WAS A QUALITY INHERITED FROM HER PARENTS, PASSED DOWN THROUGH GENERATIONS.

MARGARET'S FAMILY ON HER FATHER'S SIDE WAS DESCENDED FROM THOMAS MITCHELL OF ABERDEENSHIRE, SCOTLAND, WHO SETTLED IN GEORGIA IN 1777 IN TIME TO FIGHT IN THE AMERICAN REVOLUTION.

Family tree

RUSSELL, MARGARET'S GRANDFATHER, FOUGHT AS A CAPTAIN IN THE CONFEDERATE ARMY.

HER GREAT-GRANDFATHER ON HER MOTHER'S SIDE, PHILIP FITZGERALD, SETTLED ON A PLANTATION IN JONESBORO, GEORGIA AFTER EMIGRATING FROM IRELAND.

MARGARET MUNNERLYN MITCHELL WAS BORN TO MARY ISABELLE "MAYBELLE" STEPHENS, A WOMAN OF IRISH-CATHOLIC ANCESTRY, AND EUGENE MUSE MITCHELL, AN ATTORNEY, ON NOVEMBER 8TH, 1900.

MAYBELLE HAD THREE CHILDREN IN ALL, RUSSELL, ALEXANDER, WHOM THEY CALLED STEPHENS, AND MARGARET, BUT THE FORMER DID NOT SURVIVE HIS FIRST YEAR.

HER CHILDHOOD HOME WAS A SMALL HOUSE IN THE JACKSON HILL NEIGHBORHOOD EAST OF DOWNTOWN ATLANTA, GEORGIA.

YOUNG MARGARET FOUND HERSELF ACCIDENT PRONE. AT THE AGE OF THREE SHE CAUGHT HER DRESS ON FIRE, SO MAYBELLE MITCHELL BEGAN DRESSING HER DAUGHTER IN BOY'S PANTS.

HER BOY'S CLOTHING AND REBELLIOUS DEMEANOR QUICKLY EARNED MARGARET THE NICKNAME "JIMMY" WHICH SHE GLADLY ADOPTED UNTIL THE AGE OF FOURTEEN.

MARGARET'S MOTHER WAS A SUFFRAGETTE WHO VEHEMENTLY SPOKE OUT FOR A WOMAN'S RIGHT TO VOTE.

EQUALITY FOR WOMEN

VOTEf FOR WOMEN

Give us the vote NOW

BETWEEN MAYBELLE'S "SEEN AND NOT HEARD" APPROACH TO CHILD REARING AND HER DEDICATION TO THE CAUSE, MARGARET OFTEN FELT THAT HER MOTHER WAS NOT ACCESSIBLE AS SHE DID NOT OFTEN EXPRESS HER FEELINGS TO HER DAUGHTER.

BEFORE SHE COULD WRITE, MARGARET CONSTRUCTED ELABORATE STORIES WHICH SHE DICTATED TO HER MOTHER.

ONCE SHE BEGAN TO WRITE, SHE WOULD CRAFT HER OWN BOOKS WITH ELABORATE CARDBOARD COVERS. MARGARET WROTE WHAT SHE KNEW AND HER CHARACTERS WERE OFTEN FRIENDS AND FAMILY.

IN SEPTEMBER OF 1906 RACE RIOTS BROKE OUT IN ATLANTA FOR FOUR DAYS. THE SOUNDS OF GUNSHOTS COULD BE HEARD FOR MILES AROUND AS A MOB OF 10,000 GATHERED IN THE STREETS.

HAVING NO FIREARM, EUGENE MITCHELL STOOD WATCH OUTSIDE THE FAMILY HOME EACH NIGHT WITH A SWORD AS MAYBELLE, STEPHENS, AND A FIVE-YEAR OLD MARGARET WRESTLED WITH SLEEP.

IN 1912, EUGENE MOVED HIS FAMILY TO A LARGER HOME ON PEACHTREE STREET. MARGARET'S CHILDHOOD HOME IN JACKSON HILL BURNED IN THE GREAT ATLANTA FIRE OF 1917.

MARGARET'S TEEN YEARS WERE SPENT AT WASHINGTON SEMINARY, A PRESTIGIOUS FINISHING SCHOOL, WHERE SHE SPENT MOST OF HER TIME WRITING SHORT STORIES AND ADAPTING PLAYS, WHICH SHE DIRECTED AND OFTEN STARRED IN.

BY THE TIME WORLD WAR I BEGAN IN THE SPRING OF 1917, MARGARET WAS PREPARING TO GRADUATE HIGH SCHOOL WHEN SHE MET HER FIRST LOVE, A MILITARY MAN FROM HARVARD BY THE NAME OF LIEUTENANT CLIFFORD HENRY.

MITCHELL AND HENRY WERE ENGAGED BY THE TIME HENRY LEFT FOR FRANCE IN JULY.

IN SEPTEMBER MARGARET ARRIVED AT SMITH COLLEGE TO STUDY MEDICINE-- HER MOTHER'S DECISION--BUT SHE WAS UNCOMFORTABLE AT THE PROGRESSIVE, INTEGRATED INSTITUTION.

HER FIRST AND ONLY YEAR AT SMITH PROVED TO BE A HARD ONE. IN OCTOBER MARGARET RECEIVED WORD THAT HER FIANCÉE HAD DIED IN BATTLE.

IN JANUARY OF 1919 SHE RECEIVED YET ANOTHER LETTER THIS TIME FROM HER MOTHER, SICK WITH INFLUENZA, ASKING HER TO COME HOME.

BUT MARGARET WOULD NOT MAKE IT BACK TO GEORGIA IN TIME.

YOUR LIFE AND YOUR ENERGIES BELONG TO YOURSELF YOUR HUSBAND AND YOUR CHILDREN

ON HER DEATHBED, MAYBELLE COMPOSED A LETTER TO MARGARET LACKING IN SENTIMENT, BUT EXTOLLING THE VIRTUE OF DUTY.

AN EIGHTEEN YOUR OLD MITCHELL RETURNED TO ATLANTA AFTER ONE YEAR AT SMITH AND EMBRACED FLAPPERISM.

STRUGGLING TO MELD HER SENSE OF SELF WITH THE EXPECTATIONS OF SOUTHERN HIGH SOCIETY, MARGARET PERFORMED A RACY FRENCH TANGO AT A DEBUTANTE BALL WEARING GARTERS AND BELLS. THE STUNT LANDED HER IN THE SOCIETY PAGES—

—AND SHE WAS BLACK-BALLED BY THE JUNIOR LEAGUE, BANISHED FROM THE DEBUTANTE SCENE—A BAD GIRL OF ATLANTA'S HIGH SOCIETY.

DEPRESSION ENCOURAGED HER TO LOOK ELSEWHERE FOR ENCOURAGEMENT, AND MARGARET BEGAN SERIOUSLY DATING TWO MEN, SOMETIMES SEEING BOTH SUITORS IN THE SAME EVENING.

MITCHELL'S FIRST MARRIAGE WAS TO BERRIEN "RED" KINNARD UPSHAW, A BOOTLEGGER, IN 1922. THE MARRIAGE LASTED FOR FOUR MONTHS WHEN RED LEFT FOR THE MIDWEST.

IN THE SAME YEAR THAT SHE MARRIED RED, OUT OF NECESSITY, MARGARET BEGAN LOOKING FOR WORK. SHE WAS HIRED AS A WRITER AND EDITOR AT THE ATLANTA JOURNAL SUNDAY MAGAZINE. THE DAREDEVIL JOURNALIST ADOPTED THE NAME PEGGY MITCHELL FOR HER BYLINE.

MITCHELL, WHO STOOD JUST UNDER FIVE FOOT TALL, WAS ONE OF THE FIRST FEMALE REPORTERS FOR THE ATLANTA JOURNAL TO COVER "HARD" OR "BREAKING" NEWS OFTEN INTERVIEWING INFAMOUS INDIVIDUALS IN UNSAVORY PARTS OF TOWN AND PRISONERS ON DEATH ROW.

IN 1924 HER ANNULMENT TO RED, A RUMORED ABUSIVE HUSBAND, WENT THROUGH, AND A YEAR LATER, SHE BECAME THE WIFE OF JOHN MARSH, RED UPSHAW'S FORMER BEST-MAN.

JUST MARRIED

MARGARET AND JOHN OFTEN ENTERTAINED THE JOURNALISM CROWD IN THEIR SMALL APARTMENT WHICH THEY AFFECTIONATELY CALLED "THE DUMP." THE APARTMENT WAS ONE OF MANY IN A LARGE HOUSE ALSO ON PEACHTREE STREET.

DURING THIS TIME, MARGARET CONTINUED TO WRITE FEATURED ARTICLES FOR SUNDAY MAGAZINE IN WHICH SHE ASKED TOUGH QUESTIONS ABOUT THE ROLE OF WOMEN IN THE HOME AND WORKPLACE. SHE SAID SHE WAS TRYING TO "RESTORE WOMEN TO THEIR PROPER ROLE IN HISTORY"-

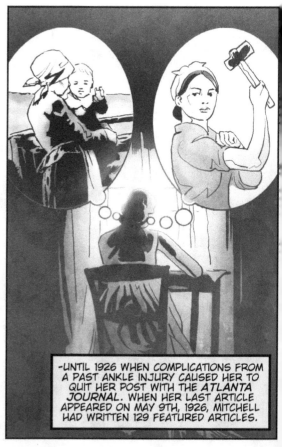

-UNTIL 1926 WHEN COMPLICATIONS FROM A PAST ANKLE INJURY CAUSED HER TO QUIT HER POST WITH THE *ATLANTA JOURNAL.* WHEN HER LAST ARTICLE APPEARED ON MAY 9TH, 1926, MITCHELL HAD WRITTEN 129 FEATURED ARTICLES.

SOME SAY THAT AT THIS TIME, MARGARET, CHILDLESS AND UNEMPLOYED, WENT INTO A DEPRESSION.

PROMPTED BY HER HUSBAND, AND BOREDOM, MARGARET BEGAN WORKING ON HER OWN BOOK. HER FIRST ATTEMPT WAS A WORK ABOUT THE JAZZ AGE THAT SHE QUICKLY ABANDONED TO WORK ON A PIECE INSPIRED BY A MEMORY FROM HER CHILDHOOD.

I DON'T WANT TO GO TO SCHOOL, MOTHER. THERE'S JUST NO REASON TO GO! IT'S A WASTE OF TIME.

THESE PEOPLE WHO OWNED THESE HOMES, THEIR WORLD HAD EXPLODED BENEATH THEM DURING THE WAR.

SOMEDAY, YOUR WORLD WILL EXPLODE BENEATH YOU. YOU HAVE TO HAVE SOMETHING TO HANG ON TO, SOMETHING WITHIN YOU TO MAKE IT THROUGH THIS LIFE, MARGARET. YOU MUST WORK WITH YOUR HANDS, BUT YOU MUST USE YOUR MIND ALSO. TO TAKE CARE OF YOURSELF, YOU MUST HAVE GUMPTION.

THIS WOULD BE THE INSPIRATION FOR MARGARET'S ONE AND ONLY NOVEL, *GONE WITH THE WIND.*

SHE WROTE THE BOOK IN REVERSE COMPLETING THE LAST CHAPTER FIRST AND FINISHING BY WRITING THE FIRST CHAPTER, BUT SHE KEPT THE NOVEL SECRET TO EVERYONE BUT HER HUSBAND WHO OFTEN SERVED AS HER EDITOR.

SHE FINISHED THE WORK RIGHT AROUND THE TIME OF THE GREAT STOCK MARKET CRASH OF 1929, BUT ABANDONED IT WITH NO INTENTION OF PUBLISHING.

BUT IN 1935, A REPRESENTATIVE FROM MACMILLAN PUBLISHING WENT ON A TALENT SCOUTING MISSION TO THE SOUTH.

GOOD AFTERNOON, MA'AM. I'M LOOKING FOR MARGARET MITCHELL. MY NAME IS HAROLD LATHAM FROM MACMILLAN PUBLISHING. I'VE BEEN TOLD YOU'RE WORKING ON A NOVEL.

I AM DOING NO SUCH THING.

WELL, I HAVE BEEN WORKING ON SOMETHING. A NOVEL. I JUST DON'T KNOW THAT IT'S READY.

YOU? WRITING A NOVEL? WELL MARGARET YOU JUST AREN'T SERIOUS ENOUGH TO WRITE A NOVEL.

TAKE THIS THING BEFORE I CHANGE MY MIND!

BUT MARGARET WAS HAVING SECOND THOUGHTS.

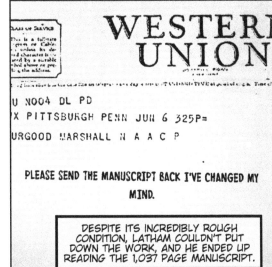

WESTERN UNION

U N004 DL PD

X PITTSBURGH PENN JUN 6 325P=

URGOOD MARSHALL N A A C P

PLEASE SEND THE MANUSCRIPT BACK I'VE CHANGED MY MIND.

DESPITE ITS INCREDIBLY ROUGH CONDITION, LATHAM COULDN'T PUT DOWN THE WORK, AND HE ENDED UP READING THE 1,037 PAGE MANUSCRIPT.

IN SIX MONTHS, THE BOOK SOLD ONE MILLION COPIES AT $3.00 EACH. CRITICS SAY THAT THE "STRUGGLE TO SURVIVE" SUBJECT MATTER OF THE BOOK SPOKE TO PEOPLE LIVING IN THE GREAT DEPRESSION.

MARGARET MITCHELL BECAME AN OVERNIGHT SENSATION.

IN 1937, MITCHELL WAS NOTIFIED BY TELEPHONE THAT SHE HAD WON THE PULITZER PRIZE FOR LITERATURE. THE FAME SHE HAD ALWAYS WANTED WAS NOW HERS, BUT IT CAME AT THE COST OF HER PERSONAL PRIVACY AND HEALTH.

IT IS RUMORED THAT MITCHELL LOST TEN POUNDS IN A MATTER OF THREE DAYS FROM THE BOOK'S PUBLICATION.

RING RING

AND THE PHONE RANG EVERY FIVE MINUTES. MARGARET DIDN'T DARE ANSWER THE PHONE.

NO, I DON'T KNOW IF MISS SCARLETT AND MR. BUTLER EVER FOUND EACH OTHER.

FOLKS SENT FAN MAIL AND COPIES OF THE BOOK TO MARGARET, AND SHE TRIED TO ANSWER EVERY LETTER AND TO SIGN EVERY BOOK MAILED TO HER. HER HUSBAND PUT A STOP TO IT WHEN HE REALIZED THE PRESSURE IT WAS PUTTING ON HER.

HOLLYWOOD CAME KNOCKING SHORTLY AFTER MITCHELL'S PULITZER WIN, AND DAVID SELEZNIK PURCHASED THE FILM RIGHTS FOR 50,000, AN ASTRONOMICAL SUM FOR THE TIME.

SELZNIK ASKED MITCHELL TO HELP HIM WRITE THE SCREENPLAY BUT SHE REFUSED FOR FEAR THAT SOUTHERNERS WOULD DISAPPROVE OF THE FILM.

IN DECEMBER OF 1939, HOLLYWOOD CAME TO ATLANTA AS THE FILM PREMIERED AT LOEW'S THEATER.

DURING A PRESS EVENT, CLARK GABLE SPOTTED MITCHELL AND SWEPT HER OFF INTO A PRIVATE ROOM. UPON EXITING GABLE SAID THAT MARGARET WAS THE MOST FASCINATING WOMAN HE HAD EVER MET.

THE FILM LATER WON TEN ACADEMY AWARDS IN TOTAL INCLUDING VIVIEN LEIGH FOR BEST ACTRESS AND A HISTORY-MAKING BEST SUPPORTING ACTRESS WIN FOR HATTIE MCDANIEL, THE FIRST AFRICAN AMERICAN TO BE NOMINATED FOR AN AWARD.

AS WORLD WAR II BEGAN, MITCHELL TOOK ON A NEW ROLE AS PHILANTHROPIST. SHE BECAME A RED CROSS VOLUNTEER WHO STUFFED BOXES FOR THE TROOPS AND RAISED MONEY FOR THE WAR EFFORT ESPECIALLY FOR THE BUILD OF THE U.S.S ATLANTA, WHICH AS A FOURTH GENERATION ATLANTA RESIDENT SHE WAS ASKED TO CHRISTEN.

ALL IN ALL, MITCHELL HELPED TO RAISE $65 MILLION DOLLARS, ENOUGH FOR TWO CRUISERS AND A DESTROYER.

I CHRISTEN THEE THE U.S.S. ATLANTA!

CRRSH

A NOW WEALTHY, BUT STILL HUMBLE MITCHELL RECEIVED A LETTER FROM DR. BENJAMIN MAYS, PRESIDENT OF THE ALL BLACK MOREHOUSE COLLEGE IN 1942 REQUESTING A SCHOLARSHIP DONATION OF $80, WHICH SHE GLADLY GAVE.

THIS WAS THE BEGINNING OF THE RELATIONSHIP BETWEEN MITCHELL AND MAYS WHO SHARED IDEAS ON EDUCATION WHILE MITCHELL FINANCIALLY SUPPORTED AFRICAN AMERICAN MEDICAL STUDENTS.

BUT DUE TO A TENSE RACIAL CLIMATE, MITCHELL'S EFFORTS REMAINED A SECRET

AND SHE ANONYMOUSLY RAISED FUNDS FOR THE FIRST PRIVATE BLACK HOSPITAL IN ATLANTA.

AFTER YEARS OF BEING IN THE SPOTLIGHT, MARGARET SOUGHT SOME QUIET TIME WHICH CAME WITH ANOTHER NEW PERSONA. SHE WANTED ONLY TO BE A SUPPORTIVE WIFE, AND SHE BEGAN TO CALL HERSELF MRS. JOHN MARSH TO AVOID THE PRESS.

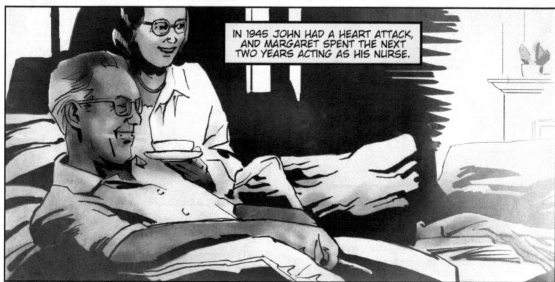

IN 1945 JOHN HAD A HEART ATTACK, AND MARGARET SPENT THE NEXT TWO YEARS ACTING AS HIS NURSE.

EVEN AFTER HIS RECOVERY, THE COUPLE REMAINED RECLUSIVE. THEY OFTEN STAYED IN AND QUIETLY WATCHED MOVIES.

UNTIL ONE NIGHT IN AUGUST OF 1949, ON THEIR WAY TO THE SHOW, MARGARET WAS HIT BY A SPEEDING CAR WHILE WALKING ON PEACHTREE STREET, BLOCKS AWAY FROM THE APARTMENT WHERE SHE WROTE HER FAMOUS NOVEL.

SHE REMAINED IN A COMA FOR SEVERAL DAYS BEFORE HER PASSING ON AUGUST 16TH, 1949.

AFTER MARGARET'S DEATH, JOHN DESTROYED THE ORIGINAL *GONE WITH THE WIND* MANUSCRIPT AS SHE HAD WISHED. A FEW CHAPTERS WERE SAVED AND LOCKED IN A VAULT IN THE EVENT THAT SOMEONE QUESTIONED MITCHELL'S AUTHORSHIP.

SOME CALL HER A FEMINIST, AND SOME SAY SHE WAS JUST A WRITER REFLECTING THE VIEWS OF HER TIME.

WHETHER YOU THINK OF HER AS A WORLD FAMOUS AUTHOR AND PHILANTHROPIST, THE EMBODIMENT OF SCARLETT O'HARA, OR THAT LITTLE GIRL IN BOY'S CLOTHING, MARGARET MITCHELL WILL ALWAYS BE REMEMBERED FOR SHOWING THE WORLD WHAT IT REALLY MEANS TO HAVE GUMPTION.

"I WAS NEVER ONE TO PATIENTLY PICK UP BROKEN FRAGMENTS AND GLUE THEM TOGETHER AGAIN AND TELL MYSELF THAT THE MENDED WHOLE WAS AS GOOD AS NEW. WHAT IS BROKEN IS BROKEN - AND I'D RATHER REMEMBER IT AS IT WAS AT ITS BEST THAN MEND IT AND SEE THE BROKEN PLACES AS LONG AS I LIVED."

Tara Broeckel — **Writer**

Martin Gimenez — **Art**

Benjamin Glibert — **Letters**

Darren G. Davis — **Editor**

Chris McFann — **Colors**

Darren G. Davis
Publisher

Maggie Jessup
Publicity

Susan Ferris
Entertainment Manager

Steven Diggs Jr.
Marketing Manager